My First Book of COUNTING FRIENDS

by Diane Stortz

Illustrated by
Kathy Couri

I'm going to the circus.
What will I see?
Come along and count with me!

1 one

one
ringmaster

See his tall hat.

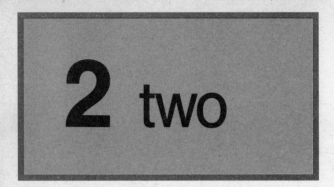

2 two

two
ticket takers

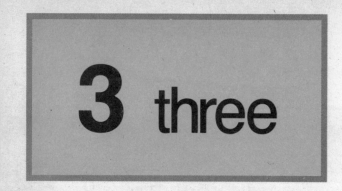

3 three

three kinds of snacks

4 four

four fantastic flyers

Hold on tight!

5 five

five elephants
on parade

I like the baby best.

6 six

six
souvenirs

7 seven

seven silly
clowns

They make me laugh!

8 eight

eight brave
acrobats

9 nine

nine prancing
ponies

10 ten

ten trained
tigers

Thank you for coming.

The show is over now.
But let's find all our
counting friends
As they take a bow.